Why I Love the Moon

Illustrated by Daniel Howarth

HarperCollins *Children's Books*

I love the moon because...

astronauts have walked there.

I love the moon because...
it changes shape.

I love the moon because...

I can see the Man in the Moon!

I love the moon because...

it pulls the oceans' tides
in and out.

I love the moon because...

sometimes there is an eclipse.

I love the moon because...

you can see it from anywhere in the world.

I love the moon because...

I can paint a picture of it.

I love the moon because...

I have a bedtime story about it.

I love the moon because...

it shines when I'm asleep.

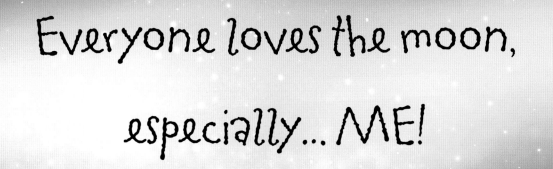

Everyone loves the moon,
especially... ME!

First published in hardback in Great Britain by HarperCollins *Children's Books* in 2019
This edition published in 2020

1 3 5 7 9 10 8 6 4 2

978-0-00-798398-8

HarperCollins *Children's Books* is a division of HarperCollins*Publishers* Ltd.

Text and illustrations copyright © HarperCollins*Publishers* Ltd 2019

A CIP catalogue record for this title is available from the British Library.
Visit our website at: www.harpercollins.co.uk

Printed and bound in China